SPECIAL SCHOOL EDITION

HOLIDAY EXPRESS

GRADE 2

AF650315

Interior illustrations by Robert Alley, Abbey Carter, Maxie Chambliss, Sue Dennen, Shelley Dieterichs, Jane Dippold, Julie Durrell, Rusty Fletcher, James Hale, Mike Moran, Sherry Neidigh, Cary Pillo, Carol Tiernon, and Lynn Vineyard

ISBN-13 978-93-5275-794-7

Printed at Polykam offset Naraina New Delhi 110028

Table of Contents

Dear Parent,

Congratulations! You hold in your hands an exceptional educational tool that will give your child a head start into the coming school year.

Inside this book, you'll find practice pages that will help your child review and learn reading and writing skills, grammar, addition and subtraction, and so much more! *Holiday Express* is divided into 6 weeks, with two practice pages for each day of the week, Monday to Friday. However, feel free to use the pages in any order that your child would like. Here are other features you'll find inside:

- A weekly **incentive chart** to motivate and reward your child for his or her efforts.
- Suggestions for fun, creative **learning activities** you can do with your child each week.
- A **recommended reading list** of age-appropriate books that you and your child can read throughout the summer.

We hope you and your child will have a lot of fun as you work together to complete this workbook.

Enjoy!
The Editors

Terrific Tips for Using This Book

1 Pick a good time for your child to work on the activities. You may want to do it around mid-morning after play or early afternoon when your child is not too tired.

2 Make sure your child has all the supplies he or she needs, such as pencils and crayons. Set aside a special place for your child to work.

3 At the beginning of each week, discuss with your child how many minutes a day he or she would like to read. Write the goal at the top of the incentive chart for the week. (We recommend reading 15 to 20 minutes a day with your child.)

4 Encourage your child to complete the worksheet, but don't force the issue. While you may want to ensure that your child succeeds, it's also important that your child maintain a positive and relaxed attitude toward school and learning.

5 After you've given your child a few minutes to look over the practice pages he or she will be working on, ask your child to tell you his or her plan of action: "Tell me about what we're doing on these pages." Hearing the explanation aloud can provide you with insights into your child's thinking processes. Can he or she complete the work independently? With guidance? If your child needs support, try offering a choice about which family member might help. Giving your child a choice can help boost confidence and help him or her feel more ownership of the work to be done.

Skill-Building Activities for Any Time

The following activities are designed to complement the six weeks of practice pages in this book. These activities don't take more than a few minutes to complete and are just a handful of ways in which you can enrich and enliven your child's learning. Use the activities to take advantage of the time you might ordinarily disregard—for example, standing in line or waiting at a bus stop. You'll be working to practice key skills and have fun together at the same time.

Finding Real-Life Connections

One of the reasons for schooling is to help children function out in the real world, to empower them with the abilities they'll truly need. So why not put those developing skills into action by enlisting your child's help with creating a grocery list, reading street signs, sorting pocket change and so on? He or she can apply reading, writing, science and Maths skills in important and practical ways, connecting what he or she is learning with everyday tasks.

An Eye for Patterns

A red-brick sidewalk, a beaded necklace, a Sunday newspaper—all show evidence of structure and organization. You can help your child recognize something's structure or organization by observing and talking about patterns they see. Your child will apply his or her developing ability to spot patterns across all school subject areas, including alphabet letter formation (writing), attributes of shapes and solids (geometry) and characteristics of narrative stories (reading). Being able to notice patterns is a skill shared by effective readers and writers, scientists and mathematicians.

Journals as Learning Tools

Most of us associate journal writing with reading comprehension, but having your child keep a journal can help you keep up with his or her developing skills in other academic areas as well—from telling time to matching rhymes. To get started, provide your child with several sheets of paper, folded in half and stapled together. Explain that he or she will be writing and/or drawing in the journal to complement the practice pages completed each week. Encourage your child to draw or write about what he or she found easy, what was difficult or what was fun. Before moving on to another set of practice pages, take a few minutes to read and discuss that week's journal entries together.

Promote Reading at Home

- Let your child catch you in the act of reading for pleasure, whether you like reading science fiction novels or do-it-yourself magazines. Store them someplace that encourages you to read in front of your child and **demonstrate that reading is an activity you enjoy**. For example, locate your reading materials on the coffee table instead of your nightstand.

- Set aside a family reading time. By designating a reading time each week, your family is assured an opportunity to discuss with each other what you're reading. You can, for example, share a funny quote from an article. Or your child can tell you his or her favorite part of a story. The key is to **make a family tradition of reading and sharing books** of all kinds together.

- **Put together collections of reading materials** your child can access easily. Gather them in baskets or bins that you can place in the family room, the car and your child's bedroom. You can refresh your child's library by borrowing materials from your community's library, buying used books or swapping books and magazines with friends and neighbors.

Skills Review and Practice

Educators have established learning standards for Maths and language arts. Listed below are some of the important skills that will help your child review and prepare for the coming school year so that he or she is better prepared to meet these learning standards.

Maths

Skills Your Child Will Review

- identifying simple fractions
- adding and subtracting through 10
- identifying coins and their values
- telling time
- identifying patterns

Skills Your Child Will Practice to Prepare for Grade Two

- identifying odd and even numbers
- adding and subtracting through 18
- adding and subtracting with regrouping
- regrouping review: ones and tens
- multiplication fact families
- adding and subtracting 2-digit numbers without regrouping
- adding and subtracting with three addends
- graphing quantities
- writing basic equations

Language Arts

Skills Your Child Will Review

- writing familiar vocabulary in manuscript writing (e.g., number words, colour words, shape words, days of the week, months of the year)
- using conventions of print in writing (e.g., capitalization and punctuation) to identify and write complete sentences
- using phonetic analysis (e.g., letter/sound relationships, beginning and ending consonants, short and long vowel sounds, consonant blends, digraphs and word patterns) to decode unknown words
- using visualization based on illustrations to augment comprehension of text
- using structural analysis (e.g., word families) to decode unknown words
- following multi-step directions

Skills Your Child Will Practice to Prepare for Grade Two

- responding to a writing prompt
- writing the names of the planets in manuscript writing
- using descriptive words to convey ideas
- constructing a variety of sentence types (e.g., statements, exclamations, commands)
- writing words within familiar word families (e.g., *-ank, -ash, -ick, -ight, -ill, -ink, -ock, -ump, -unk*)
- using parts of speech in written compositions (e.g., common nouns, proper nouns, plural nouns, present- and past-tense verbs, adjectives)
- identifying main idea, sequence of events, main characters, causes and effects
- making inferences, drawing conclusions, comparing and contrasting, classifying information
- reading for supporting details
- identifying real or fantasy within the context of story

Helping Your Child Get Ready: Week 1

These are the skills your child will be working on this week.

Maths
- adding 1- and 2-digit numbers with regrouping
- subtracting 2-digit numbers without regrouping

Reading
- classifying
- sequencing

Writing
- sentence punctuation
- proofreading

Vocabulary
- examining similarities
- sight words

Grammar
- compound nouns

Here are some activities you and your child might enjoy.

Sizzling Synonyms! The first time your child says, "It's hot outside," challenge him or her to come up with as many words as possible that mean the same thing as *hot*. You can try this with other weather words such as *rainy* or *cloudy*.

Summer Goal Suggest that your child come up with a plan to achieve a goal by the end of the summer. For example, he or she may wish to become an expert on a favorite animal or learn to count in another language. Help him or her map out a way to be successful. Periodically, check to see how your child is progressing.

Order, Order! Play a ranking game. Choose three related items and ask your child to put them in order. Ask him or her to explain the choice. For example, if you chose ice cube, snowball and frozen lake, your child might say small, medium and large; or cold, colder, coldest.

Sun Safety Talk about sun safety with your child. Ask him or her to write a list of ways to stay safe in the sun. Post it in a prominent place!

Your child might enjoy reading the following books:

Clifford the Big Red Dog
by Norman Bridwell

Cupcake Surprise: BOB Books
by Lynn Maslen Kartell

Green Eggs and Ham
by Dr Seuss

________________ 's Incentive Chart: Week 1

Name Here

This week, I plan to read __________ minutes each day.

CHART YOUR PROGRESS HERE.

Week 1	Day 1	Day 2	Day 3	Day 4	Day 5
 **I read for...**	minutes	minutes	minutes	minutes	minutes
Put a sticker to show you completed each day's work.					

Congratulations!

Wow! You did a great job this week!

Place sticker here.

Parent or Caregiver's Signature ______________________________

A–Z

Trace and write the alphabet.

A B C D E F G H I

J K L M N O P Q R

S T U V W X Y Z

Capitalising Names

Sometimes the names of people, places and things are special. They begin with a **capital letter**.

Circle the special names in the picture. Write each one correctly on a line.

1. ____________________ 2. ____________________

3. ____________________ 4. ____________________

a–z

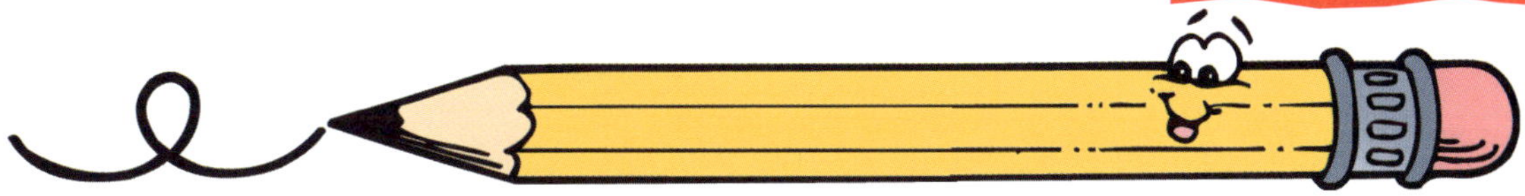

Trace and write the alphabet.

a b c d e f g h i

j k l m n o p q r

s t u v w x y z

Grouping Things

Sort the things listed below into groups. Write each word from the list in the correct box.

doll

yellow

ball

apple

bread

green

toy car

red

pasta

Look at the things in each group. How does each thing fit into the group?

Shapes on a Snake

Add or subtract.

A.  +  = 10

B.  –  = ______

C.  –  = ______

D.  +  = ______

E. 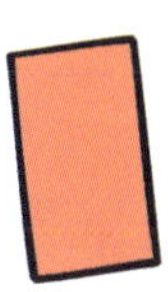 +  =

F.  + 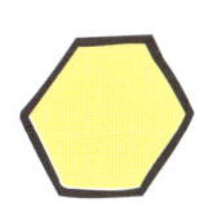 = ______

G.  + 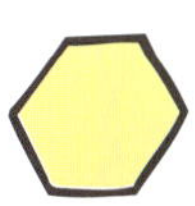 = ______

H.  +  = ______

I.  – 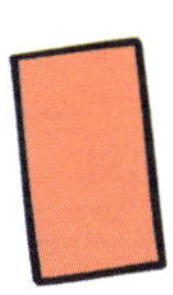 = ______

J.  – 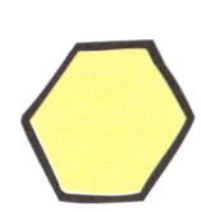 = ______

Mixed-Up Words

Words in a sentence must be in an order that makes sense.

These words are mixed up. Put them in order. Then write each sentence.

1. snow. bear likes This

2. water cold. The is

3. fast. The runs bear

4. play. bears Two

Trucks

*The **main idea** tells what the whole story is about.*

Trucks do important work. Dump trucks carry away sand and rocks. Cement trucks have a barrel that turns round and round. They deliver cement to workers who are making sidewalks. Fire trucks carry water hoses and firefighters. Gasoline is delivered in large tank trucks. Flatbed trucks carry wood to the people who are building houses.

Find the sentence in the story that tells the main idea. Write it in the circle below. Then draw a line from the main idea to all the trucks that were described in the story.

Patterns for the Mail Carrier

Meimei the mail carrier is delivering letters. Give her some help. Fill in the missing addresses on the houses below.

Extra

What pattern do you see in the house numbers? ____________

____

____

____

Going to Granny's

Kelly is going to spend the night with her grandmother. She will need to take her nightgown, a shirt and some shorts. Into the suitcase go her toothbrush, toothpaste and hairbrush. Granny told her to bring a swimsuit in case it was warm enough to swim. Mom said to pack her favorite pillow and storybooks. Dad said, "Don't forget to take Granny's sunglasses that she left here last week." Now Kelly is ready to go!

1. Colour the things that Kelly packed in her suitcase.

2. A **compound word** is a big word that is made up of two little words. For example, cow + boy = cowboy. Find 9 compound words in this story and circle them.

On a separate sheet of paper, make a list of things you would pack if you were going to spend the night at your grandmother's house.

-ank Words

Unscramble each word. Write it on the line.

nkpla ____________ ankdr ____________

ankb ____________ ktans ____________

ktan ____________ bklan ____________

canrk ____________ nkya ____________

Find and circle each word from the Word Bank.

p	r	m	b	i	n	a	t	a	n	k	i	o	h	r	s	t	a	n	k
c	k	l	b	n	k	d	r	a	n	k	r	n	a	r	t	y	j	h	j
i	l	r	b	l	a	n	k	r	i	o	n	a	c	r	a	n	k	e	w
k	a	y	a	n	k	i	b	k	r	c	a	r	n	k	y	u	r	k	n
n	k	r	n	a	f	l	a	n	k	i	c	y	x	r	p	l	a	n	k
u	r	k	n	a	k	b	a	n	k	r	n	i	s	a	n	k	v	a	k

Word Bank

bank plank
blank sank
crank stank
drank tank
flank yank

Write a sentence using one of the –ank family words.

____

____

Helping Your Child Get Ready: Week 2

These are the skills your child will be working on this week.

Maths
- adding and subtracting through 10
- problem solving
- adding double numbers to 18

Reading
- real or fantasy
- sequencing

Writing
- adjectives
- writing to a prompt

Vocabulary
- initial and final consonants
- -ash word family

Grammar
- sentence subjects and predicates

Here are some activities you and your child might enjoy.

Rainbow Hunt Ask your child to find one object for each colour of the rainbow: red, orange, yellow, green, blue and purple.

Scrambled Names Have your child write his or her first and last name on a sheet of paper and cut apart the letters. Encourage your child to use the letters to make new words. For variety, your child might also use the names of friends and family members.

Daily Time Line Help your child practice sequencing by creating a timeline of the daily routine. Encourage him or her to draw pictures or write words to describe what happened first, next and so on.

Find Your Way Home Invite your child to make a map of the place you live. He or she can draw and label what is in front, behind, to the left and to the right of your home.

Your child might enjoy reading the following books:

The Dog Who Loved Red
by Anitha Balachandran

There's a New Baby at Home
by Sumathi Sudhakar

The Gruffalo
by Julia Donaladson

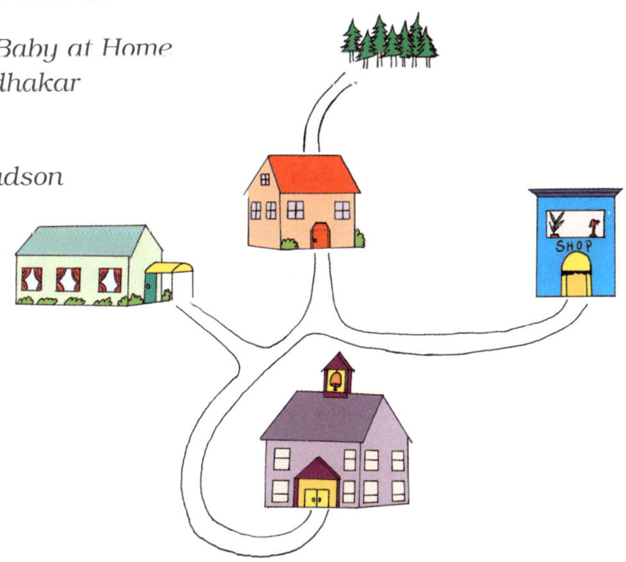

_____________________'s Incentive Chart: Week 2

Name Here

This week, I plan to read __________ minutes each day.

CHART YOUR PROGRESS HERE.

Week 2	Day 1	Day 2	Day 3	Day 4	Day 5
 I read for...	minutes	minutes	minutes	minutes	minutes
Put a sticker to show you completed each day's work.					

Congratulations!

Wow! You did a great job this week!

Place sticker here.

Parent or Caregiver's Signature ______________________________

Down the Word Steps

Work your way down the word steps.

The last letter of each word is the first letter of a new word.

Use the picture clues to help you.

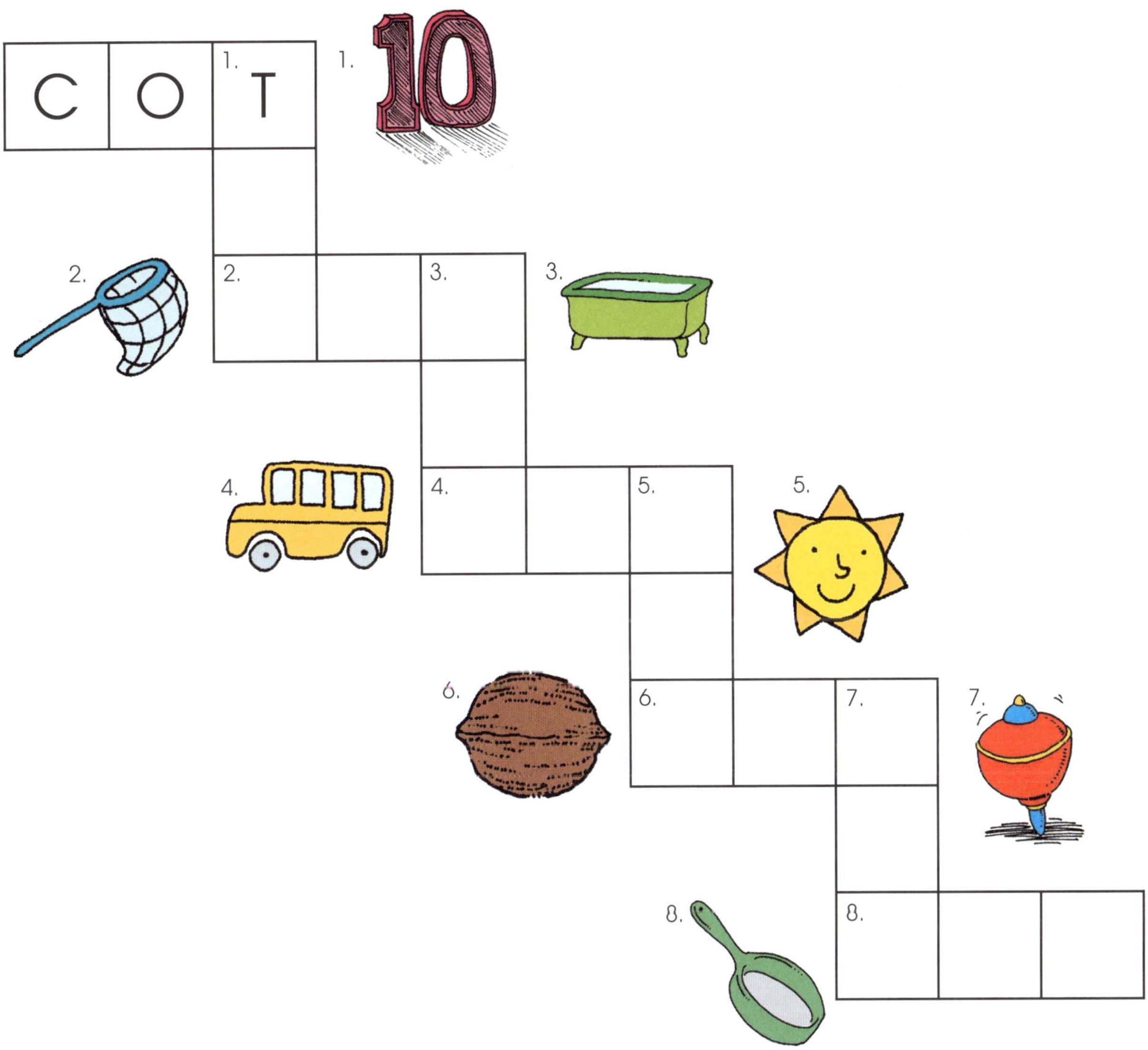

Sensational Words

Choose words from the Word Bank to describe each picture.

It tastes ______________.

It looks ______________.

It feels ______________.

It feels ______________.

It tastes ______________.

It sounds ______________.

Word Bank

bumpy
crunchy
furry
gray
red
salty
smooth
squeaky
sweet

It looks ______________.

It sounds ______________.

It feels ______________.

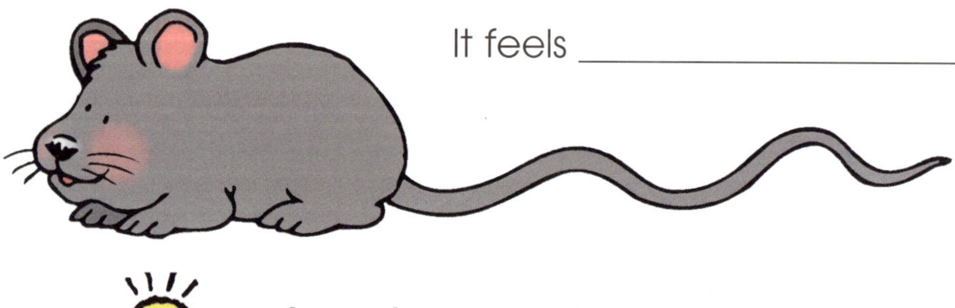

Find two objects outside. On another sheet of paper, write two adjectives to describe each object.

Mr Lee's Store

Story events that can really happen are **real**. *Story events that are make-believe are* **fantasy**.

At night, Mr Lee locked the store and went home. That's when the fun began! The ketchup bottles stood in rows like bowling pins. Then the watermelon rolled down the aisle and knocked them down. The chicken wings flew around the room. Cans of soup stacked themselves higher and higher until they laughed so hard that they tumbled over. Carrots danced with bananas. Then it was morning. "Get back in your places!" called the milk jug. "Mr Lee is coming!" Mr Lee opened the door and went right to work.

Circle the cans that are make-believe.

- ketchup bottles and a watermelon bowling
- a talking milk jug
- dancing bananas
- chicken wings that can fly all by themselves
- Mr Lee went to work.
- laughing soup cans
- Mr Lee went home at night.
- dancing carrots
- a grocery store

Draw a picture of the story on another sheet of paper.

In Warm Weather

When it is warm outside, what do you like to do?
Draw a picture to show something you like to do.

When it is warm outside, I like to ______________________________

____

I like doing this because ______________________________

____

When it is warm, I like to go to ______________________________

____

I like warm weather because ______________________________

____

Planes . . . Trains . . .

Add or subtract.

A. There are **7** cars in the parking lot. Then **3** more cars park there, too. How many cars are there in all in the lot?

7 (+) / − 3 = 10 cars

B. There are **7** boxes on the truck. Then **4** boxes fall on the street. How many boxes are left on the truck?

____ + / − ____ = ____ boxes

C. There are **10** planes waiting on the runway. Then **6** planes take off. How many planes are left on the runway?

____ + / − ____ = ____ planes

D. There are **8** girls and **2** boys on the bus. How many more girls than boys are on the bus?

____ + / − ____ = ____ more girls

E. There are **5** people in the first car and **4** people in the second car. How many people in all?

____ + / − ____ = ____ people

-ash Words

Unscramble each word. Write it on the line.

sthra ______	asmh ______
flhas ______	rhas ______
scha ______	hapssl ______
ssah ______	hcsra ______

Find and circle each word from the Word Bank.

s p x f h f r a s h x s n a g p p s h f
p s h f s n p s h f s p l a s h p s h f
c r a s h f s h n a g p p s h f c a s h
d p s r h w s a s h i r c m a s h i b v
s t a s h f g i s n a p t r a s h d s f
f g p f l a s h s n i a s m a s h b j k

Word Bank

cash sash
crash smash
flash splash
mash stash
rash trash

Write a sentence using one of the –ash family words.

______

______

Who Does It?

The **subject** of a sentence tells who or what did something.

Read the sentences below. Look at the picture to find out who or what is doing the action described in the sentence and then write it on the line.

1. A ____________________ sits in the wagon.
2. A ____________________ rides in the wagon too.
3. ____________________ is pulling the wagon.
4. Her ____________________ wants a ride too.
5. The ____________________ can carry all the animals.
6. The ____________________ fly along with them.

Write another sentence about the picture. Underline the subject of the sentence.

____

What Happens?

The **predicate** of a sentence tells what happens.

For each sentence, write an ending that tells what is happening in the picture.

1. The cat ______________________________ .

2. A mouse ______________________________ .

3. The cat ______________________________ .

4. The mouse ______________________________ .

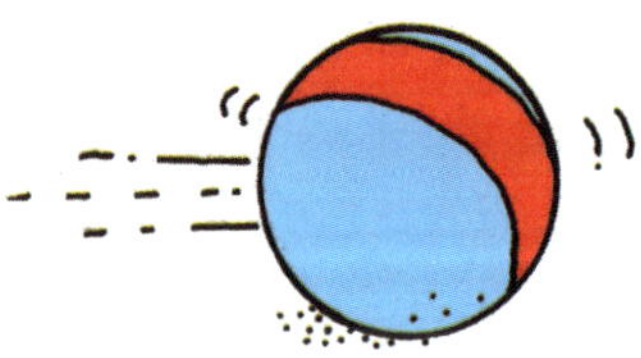

5. The ball ______________________________ .

6. The milk ______________________________ .

Write another sentence about the cat and mouse. Underline the part of the sentence that tells what happens.

____

Swimming Lessons

Sequencing *means putting the events in a story in the order they happened.*

Last summer I learned how to swim. First, the teacher told me to hold my breath. Then I learned to put my head under water. I practiced kicking my feet. While I held on to a float, I paddled around the pool. Next, I floated to my teacher with my arms straight out. Finally, I swam using both my arms and my legs. I did it! Swimming is fun! This summer, I want to learn to dive off the diving board.

Number the pictures in the order that they happened in the story.

Unscramble the letters to tell what the person in the story wants to do next.

EALNR	**OT**	**IVDE**
___ ___ ___ ___ ___	___ ___	___ ___ ___ ___

Not Far From Home

Start at . Write the number of steps to each place.
Write the number of steps back home. Add.

7 + 7 = 14

____ + ____ = ____

____ + ____ = ____

____ + ____ = ____

____ + ____ = ____

____ + ____ = ____

____ + ____ = ____

____ + ____ = ____

Helping Your Child Get Ready: Week 3

These are the skills your child will be working on this week.

Maths

- adding and subtracting through 18
- adding and subtracting with three addends

Reading

- visualizing
- making inferences

Writing

- punctuating questions

Vocabulary

- final consonants
- -ight word family

Grammar

- sentence types: telling, questions, exclamations, command

Here are some activities you and your child might enjoy.

Starring Role All children like to hear stories about themselves. Help your child feel like a star by sharing memories of him or her, finding stories with characters that have your child's name or when reading aloud to your child, insert his or her name in place of the main character's.

Compound Interest Point out examples of compound words to your child. Then have him or her keep track of the compound words heard during an hour. Try it another time and challenge your child to improve on his or her last "score."

The Case of the Mysterious Sock Invite your child to find a secret object to put in a sock. Try to guess what it is by feeling the object through the sock. Trade roles. Play again.

Start Collecting Having a collection is a great way for a child to develop higher-level thinking skills like sorting and analyzing. Encourage your child to start one. Leaves, rocks, stamps or shells are all easy and fun things to collect.

Your child might enjoy reading the following books:

Tara Cooks Up A Surprise
by Annie Besant

Everlasting Tales Volume 1
by Ken Spillman

Miss Lee and the Mosquito
by Maria Denjongpa

_______________ 's Incentive Chart: Week 3

Name Here

This week, I plan to read __________ minutes each day.

CHART YOUR PROGRESS HERE.

Week 3	Day 1	Day 2	Day 3	Day 4	Day 5
 I read for...	minutes	minutes	minutes	minutes	minutes
Put a sticker to show you completed each day's work.					

Congratulations!

Wow! You did a great job this week!

Place sticker here.

Parent or Caregiver's Signature ______________________________

Race Through the Facts

Add or subtract. The race car that ends with the highest number wins the race!

Colour the winning race car blue.

Ask Mother Goose

A sentence that asks a question ends with a **question mark** *(?). It often begins with one of these words.*

Who . . .	*Where . . .*	*Why . . .*	*Could . . .*
What . . .	*When . . .*	*Will . . .*	

Rewrite the questions using capital letters and question marks.

1. where is the king's castle

____

2. who helped Humpty Dumpty

____

3. why did the cow jump over the moon

____

4. will the frog become a prince

____

5. could the three mice see

____

A Stormy Day

Big, black clouds appeared in the sky. Lightning struck the tallest tree. The scared cow cried, "Moo!" It rained hard. Soon there was a mud puddle by the barn door. Hay blew out of the barn window.

Read the story above. Then go back and read each sentence again. Add to the picture everything that the sentences describe.

Telling Sentences and Questions

A **telling sentence** tells something. It begins with a capital letter and ends with a period.

A **question** asks something. It begins with a capital letter and ends with a question mark.

Underline the capital letter that begins each sentence. Add a period (.) if it is a telling sentence. Add a question mark (?) if it is a question.

1. The vet is nice ______
2. She helped my dog ______
3. Did she see your cat ______
4. Is the cat well now ______
5. My cat feels better ______

The order of the words in a sentence can change its meaning. Change the word order in the telling sentence to make it a question. Write the question.

6. He will take the cat home.

____

What Do You See?

Say the words.

Listen for the ending sounds.

Use the Ending Sounds Colour Code to make a picture.

Ending Sounds Colour Code

blue = s green = t black = d red = l white = m

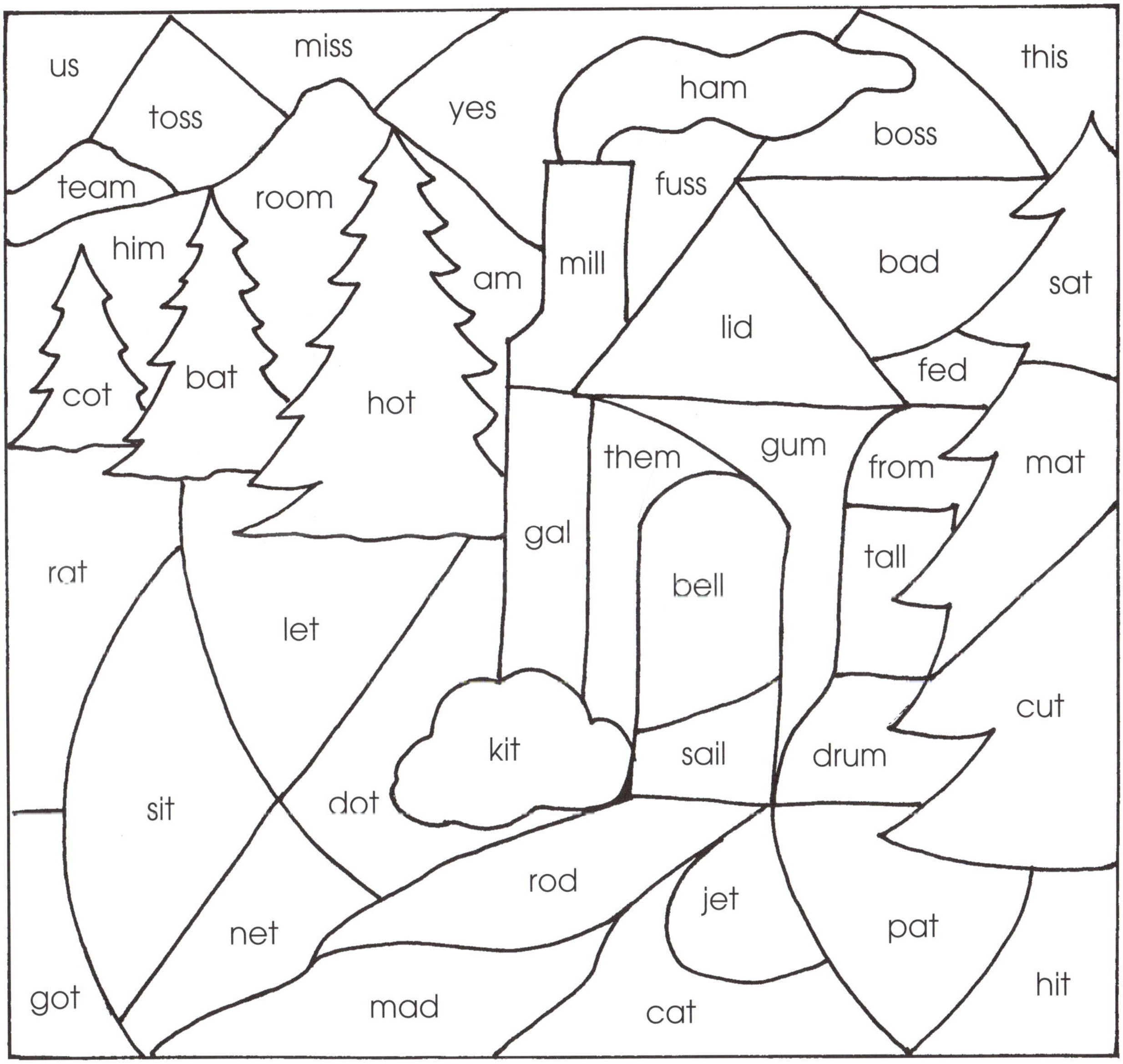

Exclamations and Commands

An **exclamation** shows strong feelings, such as excitement, surprise or fear. It begins with a capital letter and ends with an exclamation mark (!).

A **command** makes a request or tells someone to do something. It ends with a period or an exclamation mark.

Read each sentence. Write E if the sentence is an exclamation. Write C if the sentence is a command.

1. Ruby copies Angela! ______
2. Look at their dresses. ______
3. They're exactly the same! ______
4. Angela is mad! ______
5. Look at Ruby! ______
6. Show Angela how Ruby hops. ______

Write each sentence correctly.

Exclamation what a pretty dress

7. ________________________________

Command don't copy other people

8. ________________________________

A Perfect Strike

Fill in the missing number.

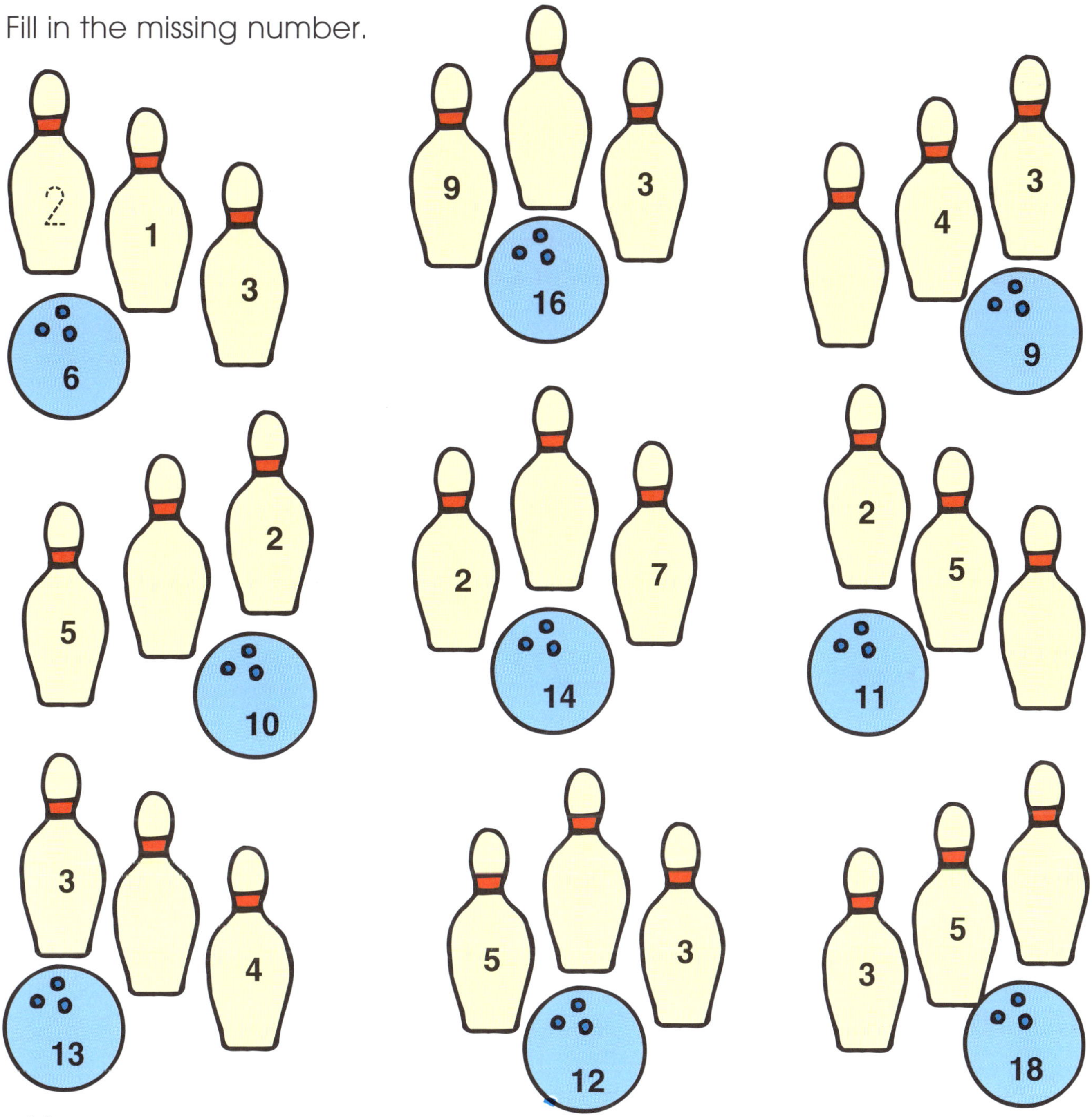

Find three different ways to make 8 with 3 numbers.

Types of Sentences; Capital I

A **telling sentence** begins with a capital letter and ends with a period.

A **question** begins with a capital letter and ends with a question mark.

An **exclamation** begins with a capital letter and ends with an exclamation mark.

A **command** begins with a capital letter and ends with a period. The word **I** is always capitalised in a sentence.

Decide if each sentence is a telling sentence, a question, an exclamation or a command. Write T, Q, E or C on the lines.

1. My sister and I went to the lake. ____
2. Come see this. ____
3. I saw three little sailboats. ____
4. Put the boat in the water. ____
5. Did I have a good time? ____
6. You bet! I loved it! ____
7. Can I go again soon? ____

What would you do at the lake? Use the word **I** and your own ideas to finish the sentences.

8. At the lake ____ saw ____________ .
9. ____ can ____________ .
10. My friend and ____ liked ____________ best.

Who Am I?

Use details from the story to make decisions about the characters.

Circle the picture that answers the riddle.

1. I have feathers. I also have wings, but I don't fly. I love to swim in icy water. Who am I?

2. I am 3 weeks old. I drink milk. I cry when my diaper is wet. Who am I?

3. I live in the ocean. I swim around slowly, looking for something to eat. I have six more arms than you have. Who am I?

4. I am an insect. If you touch me, I might bite you! I make tunnels under the ground. I love to come to your picnic! Who am I?

5. I am a female. I like to watch movies and listen to music. My grandchildren love my oatmeal cookies. Who am I?

6. I am a large mammal. I live in the woods. I have fur. I stand up and growl when I am angry. Who am I?

7. I wear a uniform. My job is to help people. I ride on a big red truck. Who am I?

-ight Words

Unscramble each word. Write it on the line.

htgfli	__________	fgriht	__________
igtknh	__________	htmig	__________
htfig	__________	thlig	__________
slhigt	__________	httig	__________

Find and circle each word from the Word Bank.

f l i g h t s p c b j k h m i g h t f h
t s i h i d f d e b j s p h s d e t r i
u y b l s i g h t t h f k n i g h t h g
f i g h t s p c b j k h x f h t i g h t
t h f r i g h t u y v b c l i g h t h t
c s l i g h t h v h f s r i g h t u t y

Word Bank

fight	might
flight	right
fright	sight
knight	slight
light	tight

Write a sentence using one of the –ight family words.

Helping Your Child Get Ready: Week 4

These are the skills your child will be working on this week.

Maths

- adding and subtracting 2-digit numbers
- coin identity and value

Reading

- compare/contrast
- comprehension

Vocabulary

- sight words
- -ill word family

Grammar

- sentence types: statements, questions
- common nouns

Handwriting

- manuscript numbers 1–10

Here are some activities you and your child might enjoy.

Word Chain Develop your child's listening skills by playing Word Chain. In this game, someone says a word and the next person must say a word that begins with the last letter of the previous player's word.

Connecting Words Give your child a word and encourage him or her to tell you the thing that often goes with it, such as peanut butter (and jelly) or thunder (and lightning). Or, make analogy pairs such as finger and hand (and toe and foot). Playing word association games can help your child build vocabulary by making connections between words.

Fruit Kebobs Your child can practice patterning by creating a tasty snack. Using a small wooden skewer and a selection of three different fruits, such as grapes, strawberries and banana slices, invite your child to create a pattern with the fruit. Encourage your child to describe the pattern to you or suggest a pattern for your child to use such as ABCABC or ABACABAC.

Now You See It, Now You Don't Show your child an interesting picture and ask him or her to look at it for a minute. Then turn the picture over and ask your child to list the objects that he or she can remember on a sheet of paper. If you wish, allow your child to look at the picture for another minute to help him or her add more items to the list.

Your child might enjoy reading the following books:

Elmer and Wilbur
by David McKee

Discover More: Things That Go
by Penelope Arlon

The Berenstain Bears Too Much TV
by Stan and Jan Berenstain

_______________ 's Incentive Chart: Week 4

Name Here

This week, I plan to read _______________ minutes each day.

CHART YOUR PROGRESS HERE.

Week 4	Day 1	Day 2	Day 3	Day 4	Day 5
 I read for...	minutes	minutes	minutes	minutes	minutes
Put a sticker to show you completed each day's work.					

Congratulations!

Wow! You did a great job this week!

Place sticker here.

Parent or Caregiver's Signature _______________________________

Riddle Fun

Compare *means to look for things that are the same.*
Contrast *means to look for things that are different.*

To solve the riddles in each box, read the clues in the horse. Then write the letters in the blanks with the matching numbers.

What kind of food does a racehorse like to eat?

___	___	___	___		___	___	___	___
11	5	10	3		11	9	9	2

1. What letter is in LOG, but not in DOG?
2. What letter is in DIME, but not in TIME?
3. What letter is in BITE, but not in BIKE?
4. What letter is in WEST, but not in REST?
5. What letter is in FAN, but not in FUN?
6. What letter is in BOX, but not in FOX?
7. What letter is in CAR, but not in CAN?
8. What letter is in ME, but not in MY?
9. What letter is in SOCK, but not in SACK?
10. What letter is in SEE, but not in BEE?
11. What letter is in FULL, but not in PULL?

What does a rose sleep in at night?

___	___	___	___	___	___		___	___	___
11	1	9	4	8	7		6	8	2

Camp Fiddlestick

A telling sentence is called a **statement**. *An asking sentence is called a* **question**. *Now ask yourself:*

How do sentences begin? How do statements end? How do questions end?

Write three statements and three questions about the picture.

Statements:

1. ______________________________

2. ______________________________

3. ______________________________

Questions:

1. ______________________________

2. ______________________________

3. ______________________________

Sort It Out!

Put each word from the Word Box in the circle where it belongs. We did the first one for you.

Word Box

~~ask~~	funny	short
brother	said	children
pretty	brown	took
purple	say	sister
read	school	white

People, Places and Things
(nouns)

____
____
____
____
____

Action Words
(verbs)

ask
____
____
____
____

Describing Words
(adjectives)

____
____
____
____
____

Snuggle Up With a Book

Day of the Week	Reading Minutes
Sunday	97
Monday	28
Tuesday	73
Wednesday	44
Thursday	51
Friday	45
Saturday	80

Use the chart to answer the questions.

A. What day did Alex read for the longest time?

____

B. How many minutes did Alex read on Wednesday and Friday? ______ minutes

C. What day did Alex read for the shortest time?

____

D. How many more minutes did Alex read on Sunday than Tuesday? ______ minutes

E. How many minutes did Alex read on Monday and Thursday? ______ minutes

F. How many more minutes did Alex read on Tuesday than Thursday? ______ minutes

One hour is 60 minutes. On what days did Alex read longer than one hour?

______________, ______________, ______________

Number Words

Trace and write.

1 one

2 two

3 three

4 four

5 five

More Number Words

Trace and write.

6 six

7 seven

8 eight

9 nine

10 ten

Money Matters

Alex asked his little brother Billy to trade piggy banks.

Alex's bank has these coins and notes: Billy's has these coins and notes:

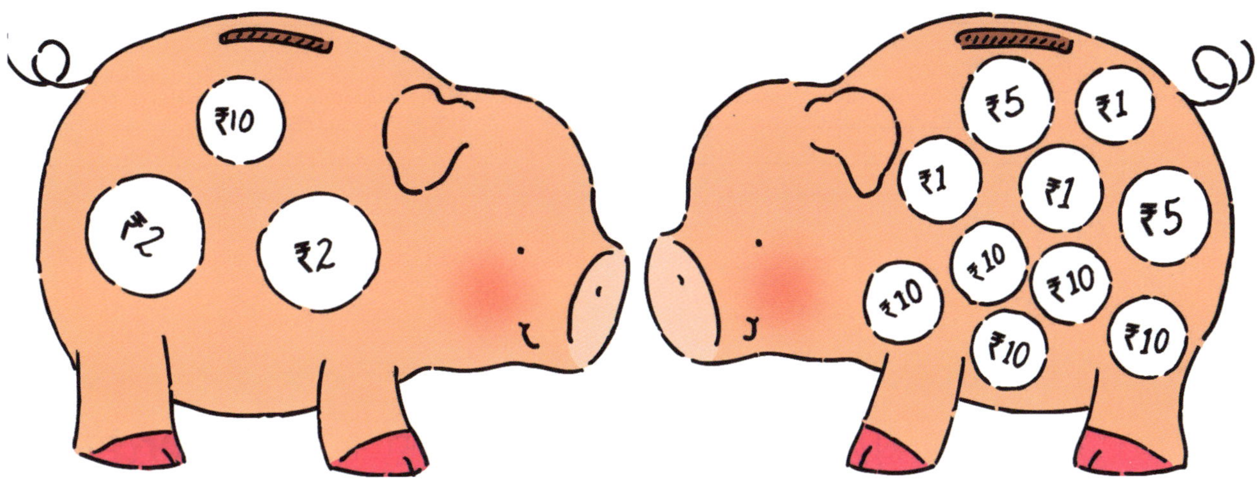

Do you think this is a fair trade? ______________________________

Test your answer:

Add up Alex's money: ______________________________

Add up Billy's money: ______________________________

Write the totals in this Greater Than/Less Than equation:

______________________ > ______________________

Who has more money?______________________________

-ill Words

Unscramble each word. Write it on the line.

blil	______	lwil	______
lhil	______	liqul	______
ildrl	______	lichl	______
irlgl	______	lsil	______

Find and circle each word from the Word Bank.

t c l h l h f q u i l l s p x f h t h f
c h i l l u y l l b l h i l l t h f h l
c x f h d r i l l t h h f g r i l l s p
s i l l s l p l f c l h h b i l l j k y
t l h f w i l l u c b v b l t h r i l l
u l b l j k y v l c l h l b l m i l l u

Word Bank

bill mill
chill quill
drill sill
grill thrill
hill will

Write a sentence using one of the –ill family words.

____

____

People, Places and Things

Common nouns name people, places or things.

Read each sentence. Circle the common nouns.

1. The boy made a boat.
2. The brothers went to the park.
3. A girl was with her grandmother.
4. Two boats crashed in the lake.
5. Friends used a needle and thread to fix the sail.

Write the common nouns you circled under the correct heading below.

People	Places	Things
____________	____________	____________
____________	____________	____________
____________		____________
____________		____________
____________		____________

Story Comprehension

Read the story. Then answer each question.
Fill in the bubble next to the best answer.

Cats and dogs are good pets. You can find these pets in many homes.

A cat is a good pet. A cat can run and jump. A cat can play with a ball of yarn. A cat can also lick your hand.

A dog is a good pet too. A dog can chase after a ball. A dog can jump up and catch a stick. A dog can also help keep you safe.

1. What two animals make good pets?
   - O cats
   - O dogs and sharks
   - O dogs and cats

2. What is a good title (name) for this story?
   - O Good Pets
   - O Cats at Home
   - O Pet Food

3. What can both cats and dogs do?
   - O jump up and catch a stick
   - O keep you safe
   - O run and jump

Helping Your Child Get Ready: Week 5

These are the skills your child will be working on this week.

Maths

- telling time
- adding 2-digit numbers without regrouping

Reading

- real or fantasy
- sequencing

Writing

- writing to a prompt

Vocabulary

- long vowels
- -ock word family

Grammar

- plural nouns

Handwriting

- manuscript days of the week

Here are some activities you and your child might enjoy.

Who Is It? Play a guessing game. Give your child clues about someone your family knows. Can he or she guess this person's identity? Trade roles. Play again.

What's My Sign? When you go places with your child, ask him or her to look around and record as many signs and symbols as possible and then share the list. Discuss why some road signs do not have words and others do. Encourage your child to make up his or her own "road signs" to post around your home.

Two-Minute Lists Give your child two minutes to list as many plural words as he or she can think of that end with the letter *s*.

Summer Games Plan a mini "Summer Olympics" with your family. Play classic picnic games such as a water-balloon toss or a three-legged race or make up fun games of your own. Take turns trying them!

Your child might enjoy reading the following books:

Come See the Sensational Safety Puppet Show
by Kimberly McArthur

Curious George
by HA Rey

Scholastic Young Classics: The Crow and the Eagle

_______________'s Incentive Chart: Week 5

Name Here

This week, I plan to read _______________ minutes each day.

CHART YOUR PROGRESS HERE.

Week 5	Day 1	Day 2	Day 3	Day 4	Day 5
 I read for...	minutes	minutes	minutes	minutes	minutes
Put a sticker to show you completed each day's work.					

Congratulations!

Wow! You did a great job this week!

Place sticker here.

Parent or Caregiver's Signature _______________________________

Days of the Week

Trace and write.

Sunday

Monday

Tuesday

Wednesday

Thursday

Friday

Saturday

Picture Maze

Can you get to the end of this maze?
Say the picture names. Listen for the sound of long *a*.
Colour the picture if the name has the long-*a* sound.

Start

Finish

More Than One

Many nouns or naming words, add **-s** to show more than one.

Read the sets of sentences. Draw a line under the sentence that has a naming word that names more than one.

1. Jan has her mittens.
   Jan has her mitten.

2. She will run up a hill.
   She will run up hills.

3. Jan runs with her dogs.
   Jan runs with her dog.

4. The dogs can jump.
   The dog can jump.

Look at each picture. Read each word. Write the plural naming word that matches the picture.

5. 

cat ____________________

6. 

sock ____________________

Fun at the Farm

Story events that can really happen are **real***. Story events that are make-believe are* **fantasy***.*

Read each sentence below. If it could be real, colour the picture. If it is make-believe, put a X on the picture.

Dairy cows give milk.

The pig said, "Let's go to the dance tonight!"

The hay was stacked in the barn.

The green tractor ran out of gas.

The goat and the sheep got married by the big tree.

Four little ducks swam in the pond.

The farmer planted pizza and hamburgers.

The mouse ate the dinner table.

The newborn calf walked with wobbly legs.

Two crickets sang "Mary Had a Little Lamb."

Rain made the roads muddy.

The farmer's family ate a pie.

On another sheet of paper, write one make-believe sentence about the farmer's house and one real sentence about it.

More Than One

A **plural** noun names more than one person, place or thing.
To make most nouns plural, add an **-s**.

Study the picture. Read the words. Write the plural of the word if there is more than one in the picture.

One	More Than One	One	More Than One
1. girl	______________	7. ball	______________
2. boy	______________	8. hoop	______________
3. doll	______________	9. man	______________
4. lion	______________	10. cap	______________
5. poster	______________	11. shirt	______________
6. balloon	______________	12. hand	______________

Write a sentence using one of the plural nouns.

____

____

All About Ice Cream

Draw the tallest ice cream cone you can in the box.

Write three things you know about ice cream. Use the words in the Word Bank if you need help.

1. ______________________________

2. ______________________________

3. ______________________________

WORD BANK

cold	tasty
flavours	cone
colours	chocolate
melts	vanilla
sweet	yummy

If you could invent an ice cream flavour, what would it be?

____

____

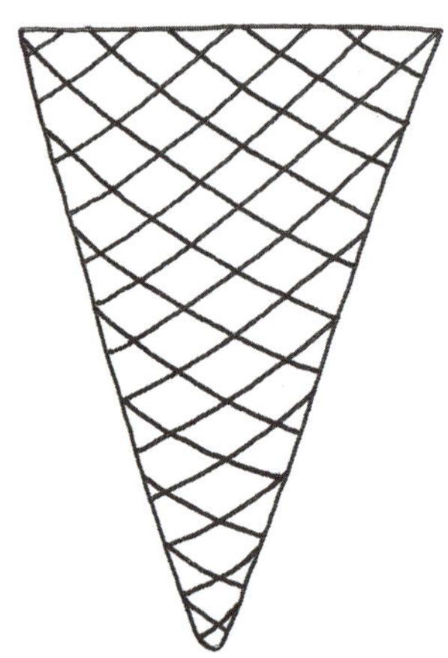

Counting on Good Manners

Add. Then use the code to write a letter in each oval to find the "good manner" words.

11 + 10	62 + 31	44 + 34	41 + 5	13 + 31	35 + 43

40 + 10	43 + 24	42 + 4	54 + 25	41 + 42

57 + 2	22 + 3	34 + 32

54 + 5	21 + 4	41 + 25	21 + 11	26 + 52

50 + 30	70 + 8	50 + 43	11 + 7	15 + 10	31 + 4	17 + 61

Code

18 C	21 P	25 O	32 R	35 M	44 S	46 A	50 T
59 Y	66 U	67 H	78 E	79 N	80 W	83 K	93 L

-ock Words

Unscramble each word. Write it on the line.

crko ________	kfcol ________
skoc ________	okknc ________
cosmk ________	cclok ________
olkc ________	dkoc ________

Find and circle each word from the Word Bank.

s p b j k x f h r o c k u c h y u v b l
l o c k u y c k v c k b l f l o c k i y
t h c k b j k h f k n o c k t h c k i f
f r o c k s p x b j k f h s o c k t h f
c l o c k t c h h c k f d o c k x f c k
t b j k h f c r o c k s p h s m o c k k

Word Bank

clock	knock
crock	lock
dock	rock
flock	smock
frock	sock

Write a sentence using one of the –ock family words.

____

____

A Pencil Sandwich?

How does the lead get inside a wooden pencil? Pencils are made out of strips of wood cut from cedar trees. Then grooves are cut in the strips. Graphite is laid into the grooves. (We call it lead, but it is really graphite.) Then another strip of wood is glued on top of the first one, making a pencil sandwich! The wood is rounded in rows on the top strip of wood and the bottom strip. Then the pencils are cut apart and painted. An eraser is added on the end and held in place by a metal ring. When you buy a pencil, you sharpen it and then you are ready to write.

Look at the pictures. Number them in the order that they happen in the story.

☐ 
graphite added

☐ 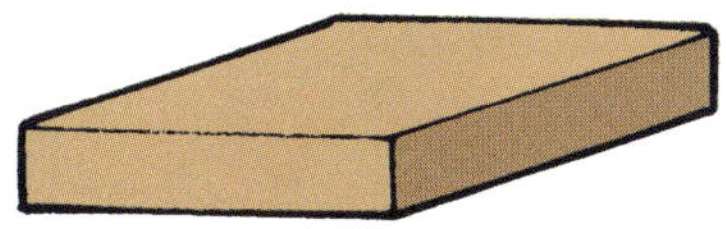
strips of wood

☐ 
pencil sandwich

☐ 
grooves

☐ 
cut apart and painted

☐ 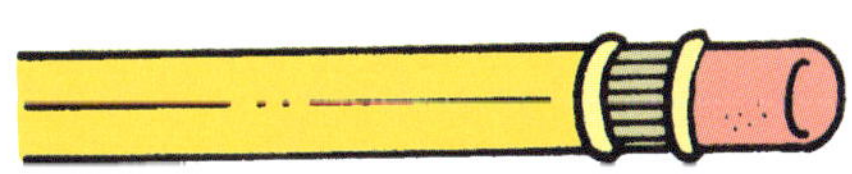
eraser added

☐ 
rounded on top and bottom

☐ 
sharpen

Clock Work

Draw the hands on the clock so it shows 4:00.

Draw the hands on the clock so it shows 4:30.

What do you do at 4:00 in the afternoon? Write about it on the lines below.

Draw the hands on the clock so it shows 6:00.

Draw the hands on the clock so it shows 6:30.

What do you do at 6:00 in the evening? Write about it on the lines below.

Helping Your Child Get Ready: Week 6

These are the skills your child will be working on this week.

Maths
- subtracting 2-digit numbers without regrouping
- regrouping review: ones and tens

Reading
- classifying
- making predictions

Vocabulary
- long and short vowels
- -ump word family

Grammar
- verbs

Handwriting
- manuscript months of the year

Here are some activities you and your child might enjoy.

Less Is More Provide your child with a reclosable bag containing 20 fifty-paise coins, 10 one-rupee coins and 5 two-rupee coins. Encourage him or her to count the fifty-paise coins by arranging them into groups of 5. Explain that a rupee is worth 100 paise and two rupees equals 4 fifty-paise coins. Ask questions such as *How many paise equals 5 rupees? Which is worth more: a two-rupee coin or 2 fifty-paise coins?*

Simon Says This favourite game can be used to practice specific skills or concepts such as prepositions. For example, say *Simon says, "Put your hands* behind *your back,"* or *Simon says, "Walk* across *the room,"* or *"Put your palm* under *your chin."* Remind your child to follow instructions only when "Simon Says."

Sidewalk Chalkboard Your child may find practicing spelling words or handwriting more like play when using colourful sidewalk chalk outdoors. Challenge your child to write words as big as possible, then as small as possible.

Surprise Story Cut out ten pictures from a magazine. Put them in a bag. Invite your child to take them out one at a time to tell a story.

Your child might enjoy reading the following books:

Where the Wild Things Are
by Maurice Sendak

Song of the Bookworm
by Anushka Ravishankar

Small Piglet Looks for Mommy
by Scholastic India

________________________'s Incentive Chart: Week 6

Name Here

This week, I plan to read ________________ minutes each day.

CHART YOUR PROGRESS HERE.

Week 6	Day 1	Day 2	Day 3	Day 4	Day 5
 I read for...	minutes	minutes	minutes	minutes	minutes
Put a sticker to show you completed each day's work.					

Congratulations!

Wow! You did a great job this week!

Place sticker here.

Parent or Caregiver's Signature ________________________________

Colour the Bowtie

Do the subtraction problems in the picture below. Then use the Colour Key to tell you what colour to mark each answer with.

Colour Key

14 = pink
47 = yellow
26 = purple
63 = green
33 = blue

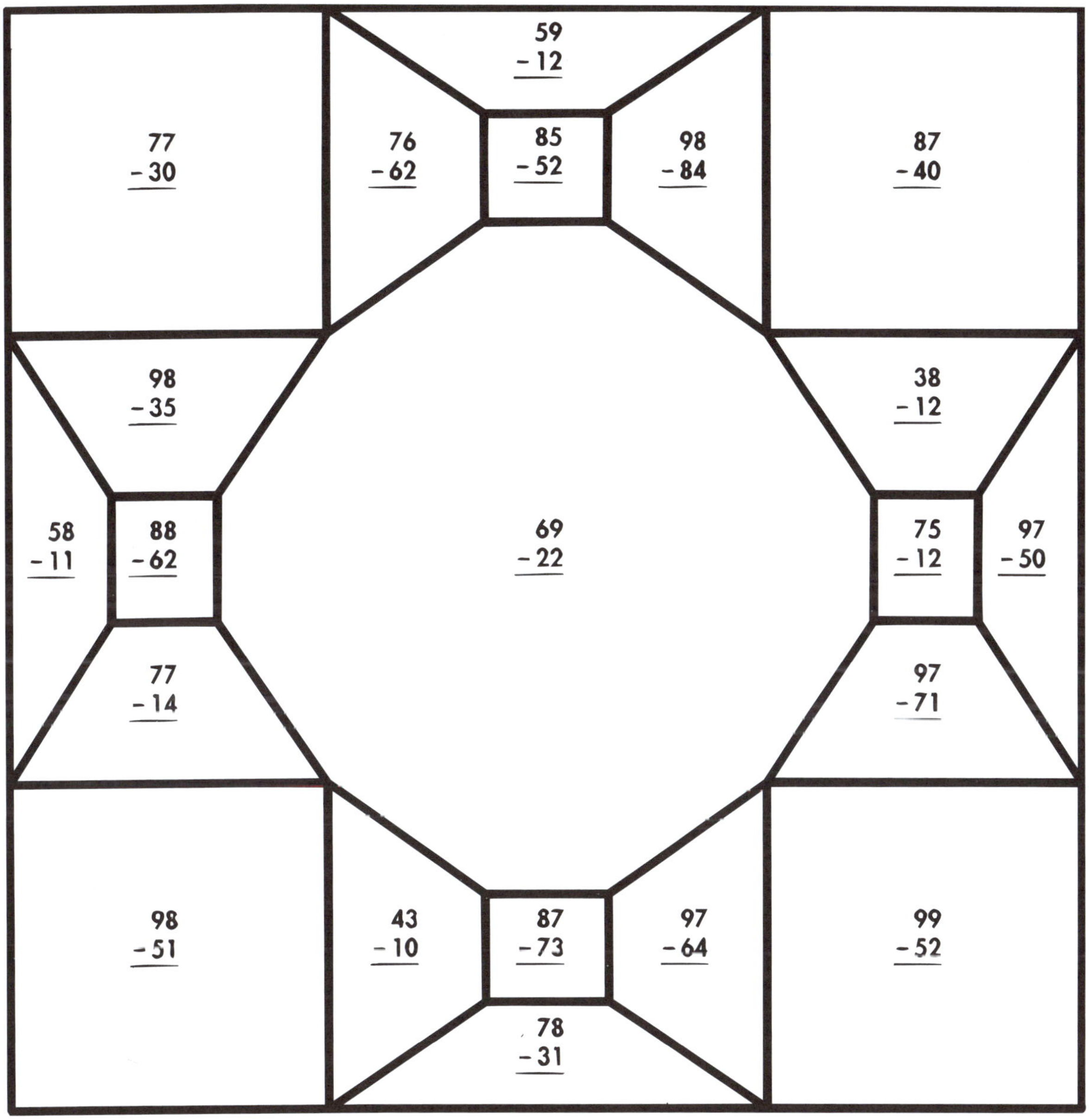

On another sheet of paper, draw a picture of four of your friends or family members. Give each one a bowtie!

What's Missing?

Something is missing from each picture. Read the clues and look at the pictures carefully to find out what it is. Say the name of each missing item and add it to the picture.

1.
Clue: long *i*
You fly it.

2.
Clue: short *i*
You play on it.

3.
Clue: long *a*
You put flowers in it.

4.
Clue: short *a*
You hit a ball with it.

5.
Clue: long *e*
You need two.

6.
Clue: short *e*
You sleep on it.

7.
Clue: long *o*
You drive on it.

8.
Clue: short *o*
You wear it on your foot.

9.
Clue: short *u*
You drink from it.

Months

Trace and write.

January

February

March

April

May

June

Months

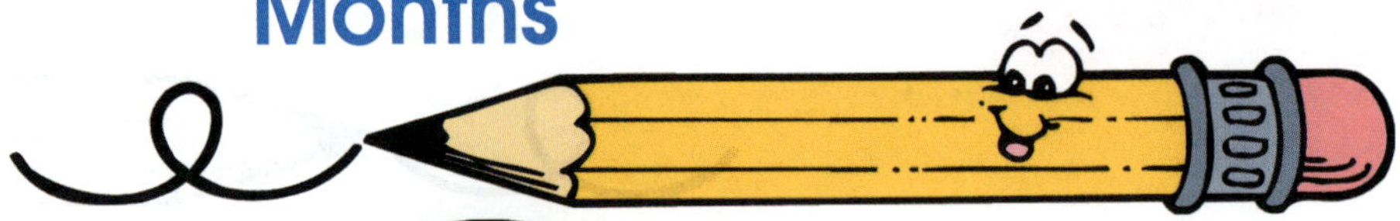

Trace and write.

July

August

September

October

November

December

Summer Vacation

Grouping like things together helps you see how parts of a story are connected and makes the story easier to understand.

Last summer, Dad, Mom, Tim and Tara went to the beach in Goa. They swam, fished, built sandcastles and went sailing. Mom brought a picnic lunch. She spread a blanket on the sand and set out chicken sandwiches, potato chips, apples and cookies. She brought lemonade in the cooler. Later, Tim and Tara walked along the beach and saw a crab walking sideways. A stray dog was barking at it. A starfish had washed up on the beach too. Tim threw bread crumbs up in the air to feed a flock of seagulls. Then the family went back to the hotel and Tim and Tara played video games until bedtime.

Use the story to find the answers. Fill in the blanks.

Picnic Items

____
____
____
____

People Who Went to the Beach

____
____
____
____

What They Did

____
____
____
____

Living Things They Saw on the Beach

____
____
____
____

A Great Catch

Circle each group of 10. Write the number of tens and ones on the chart. Then write the number on the baseball glove.

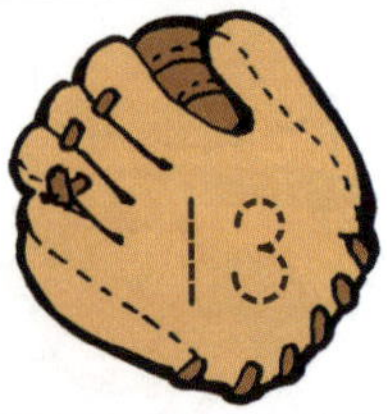

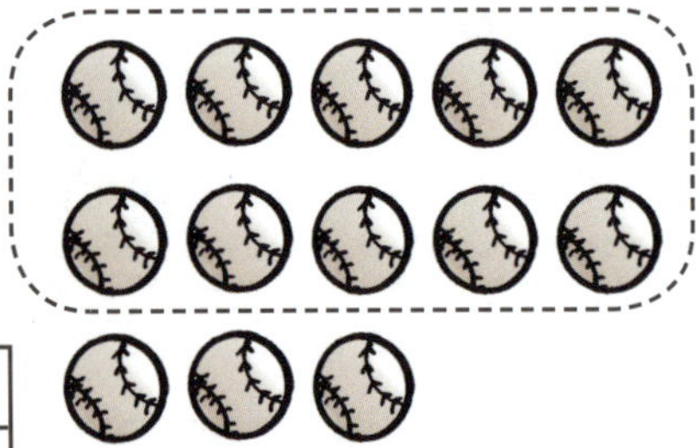

tens	ones
1	3

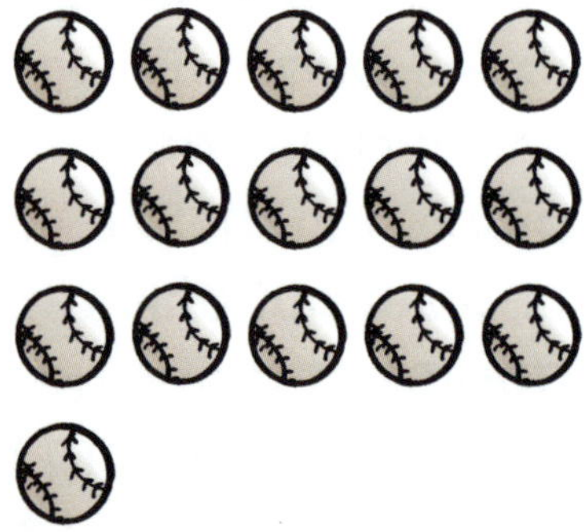

tens	ones

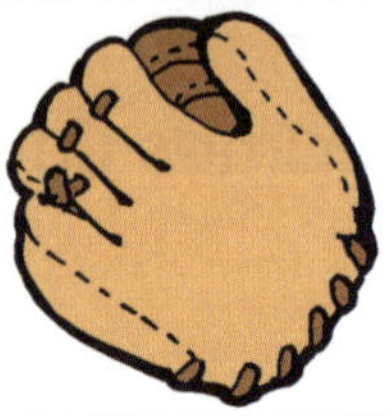

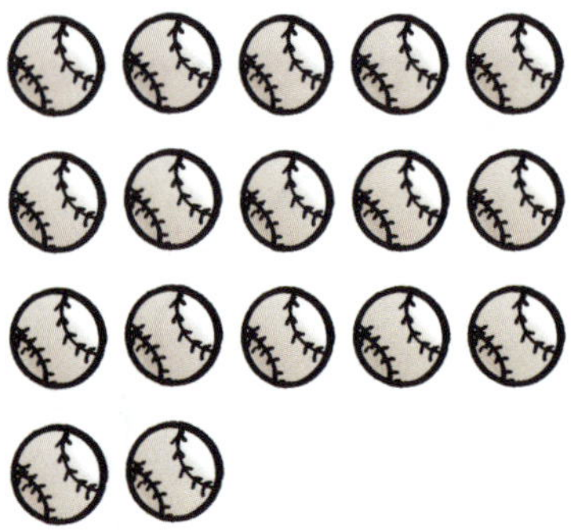

tens	ones

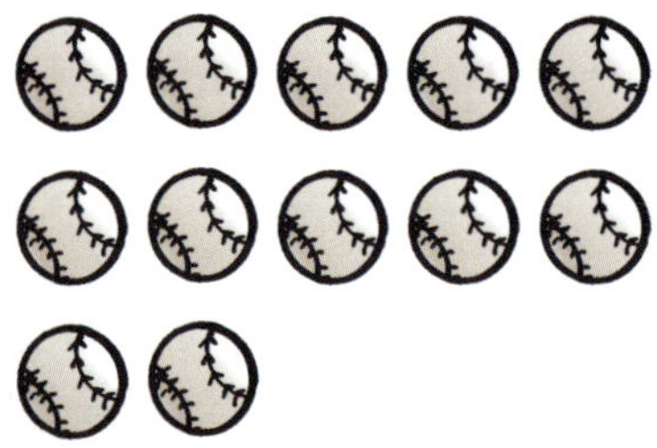

tens	ones

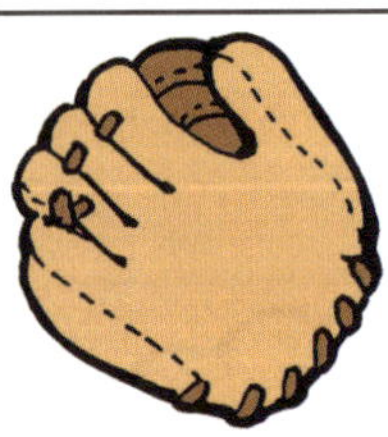

tens	ones

tens	ones

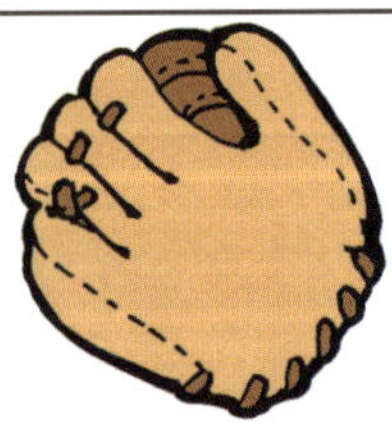

tens	ones

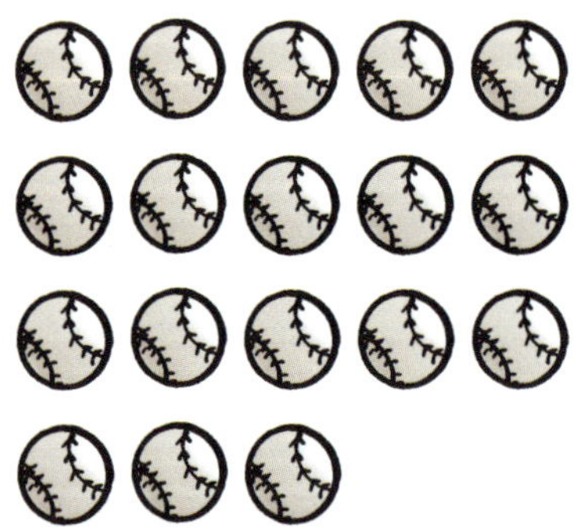

tens	ones

Will He Be Alright?

Use story details to guess what will happen next.

Father Eagle said to his young son, "Today is a very special day. You will fly for the first time." Baby Eagle was afraid. He said, "But Father, I don't know how. What should I do?" His father laid a strong wing on his little shoulder and said, "You will know." They stood at the edge of a very high cliff. Far below were huge rocks and a canyon. "Ride the wind, my son!" said Father Eagle, and he gently pushed his son off the cliff. Baby Eagle yelled, "Help! Help!" and wildly flapped his wings. All of a sudden something wonderful happened!

1. What do you think happened next? Colour the rock that tells the most likely answer.
2. Why did you choose that answer? Find the sentence in the story that gives you a hint that the story has a happy ending. Write it here.

____

____

Unscramble the words and write the answers: **ODPRU** **AARDFI**

3. How do you think Baby Eagle felt at first when he was pushed off the cliff? ________________
4. How do you think Father Eagle felt at the end of the story? ________________

Action at Practice

A **verb** is an action word. It tells what someone or something is doing.

Read each sentence. Write the action verb in the telling part of the sentence.

1. Ronald runs to the field. ______________
2. Michael wears a batting helmet. ______________
3. He smacks the ball hard. ______________
4. Ronald holds the wrong end of the bat. ______________
5. He misses the ball. ______________
6. Michael waits to take a run. ______________
7. Ronald hits the ball. ______________
8. He takes two runs. ______________

Write a sentence about the picture. Use an action verb and circle it.

____

____

____

Action at the Game

A **verb** is an action word. It tells what someone or something is doing.

Draw a line to match each sentence with an action verb. Then write the action verbs on the lines to finish the sentences.

1. Moms and dads ________________ the game.	throws
2. The bowler ________________ the ball.	opens
3. Ronald ________________ his eyes.	watch
4. The team ________________ for Ronald.	cheers
5. Ronald ________________ the ball past the bowler.	runs
6. He ________________ to the non-striker's end.	hits
7 Someone ________________, "Go, Ronald, go!"	eat
8. The kids ________________ ice cream after the game.	yells

-ump Words

Unscramble each word. Write it on the line.

mpbu ____________ mphu ____________

rupmg ____________ ppum ____________

pjum ____________ muppl ____________

umpst ____________ mpdu ____________

Find and circle each word from the Word Bank.

u y c h v b l s t u m p s p x p l u m p
f h u m p u c h y v f h b l j u m p p m
o p g m h b u m p m p c h g r u m p s t
j s d b n h k m p p u m p s p m p x f h
d u m p t h c h f c l u m p w s p x f h
t c m p e r c a b t h j k h h f l u m p

Word Bank

bump jump
clump lump
dump plump
grump pump
hump stump

Write a sentence using one of the –ump family words.

____

____

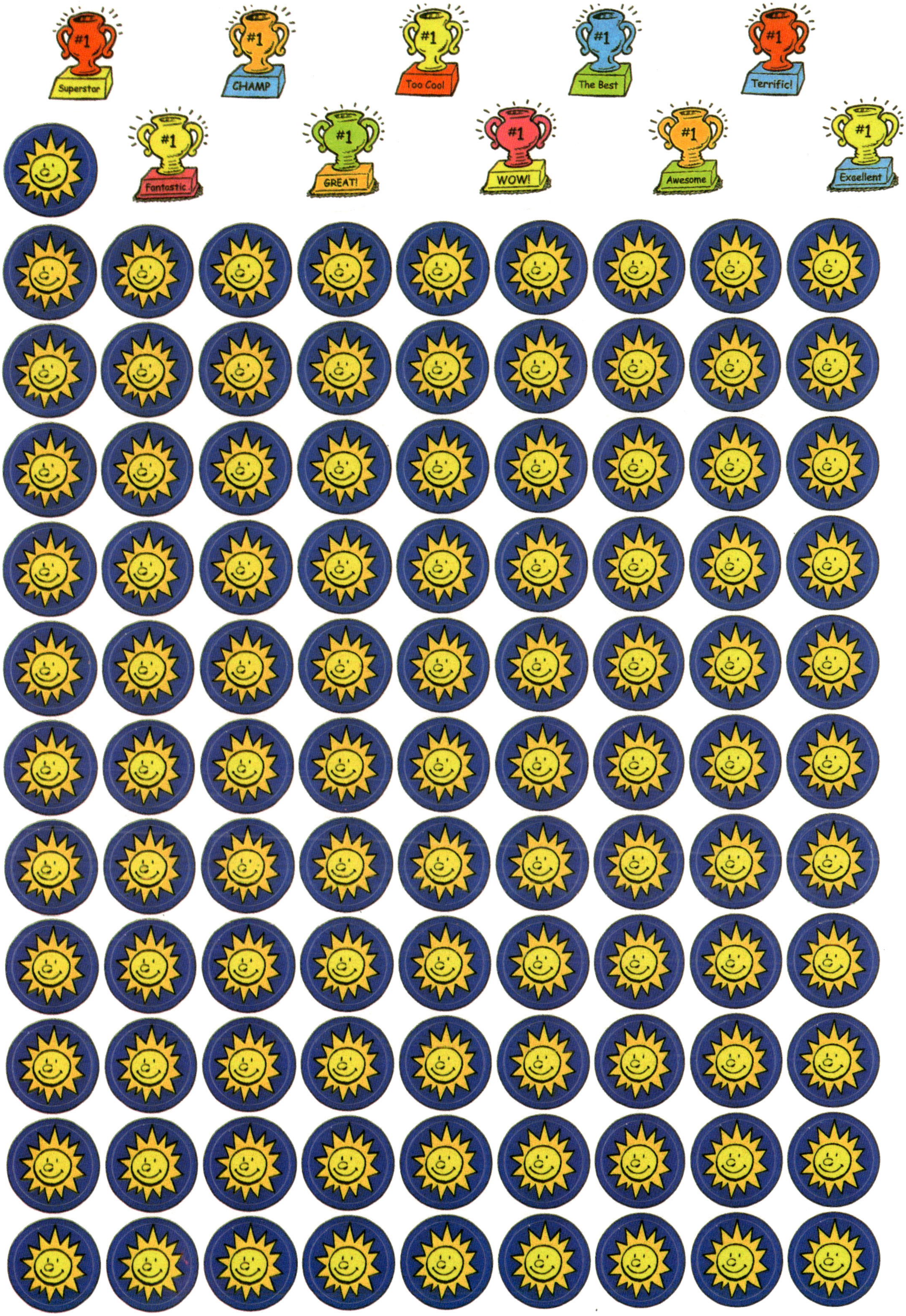
#1
Superstar
#1
CHAMP
#1
Too Cool
#1
The Best
#1
Terrific!
#1
Fantastic
#1
GREAT!
#1
WOW!
#1
Awesome
#1
Excellent